The Zipper

written and illustrated by

David Dickson

The Characters

Nathan
That's me.

Owen

Nick

The Setting

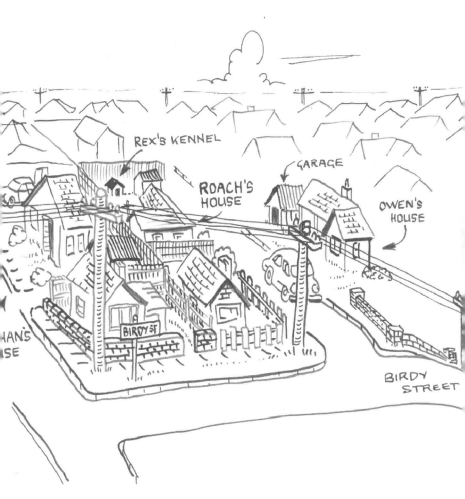

CONTENTS

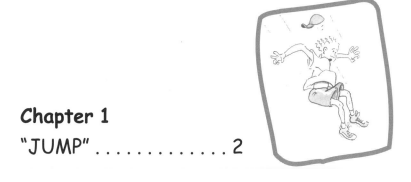

CHAPTER 1

"JUMP!"

"Jump. Come on ... I dare you ... Jump!"

I was perched on the garage roof at Owen's place. Owen and Nick were standing on the path below me.

"Come on, Nathan," said Owen. "We haven't got all day."

"OK ... OK ..." I said, and had another look over the edge.

It was the summer holidays and we had been playing cricket. I had hit the ball onto the roof.

"Come on," said Nick. "What are you waiting for?"

"Yeah, come on," said Owen. "Jump. It's not far."

The path below was made of concrete.
Owen had jumped down from here last
week for a dare.

"Are you scared, or what?"

"No," I answered.

Owen did a pretend yawn, a very loud one. He turned to Nick. "He's going to be up there all day. Let's go and watch TV."

"Wait," I said. "Don't go ... I'll jump." I silently counted up to ten. I closed my eyes and jumped.

"Oooo ..." I moaned.

"Are you all right?" they asked together.

I couldn't answer. "Oooooo ..." My ankle felt as if it had been whacked with a hammer.

"Are you OK?" they asked again.

"Mmm ..." I nodded. I couldn't speak.
I was afraid I'd start crying.

I rolled my sock down to look at my ankle. It was starting to swell up. "Maybe it's broken," I moaned.

That night, Dad sat on the end of my bed. "The X-ray showed nothing broken. But the doctor said it's a very nasty sprain."

"Why did you do a stupid thing like jumping off a roof?" he asked.

"I didn't want Owen and Nick to think I was chicken," I said.

"You what?" He shook his head in disbelief. "You jumped off the roof just so your mates wouldn't think you're a chicken? Are you crazy or something?"

I said nothing. There was a long silence. I was surprised he got so angry. After all, he wasn't the one who had got hurt.

CHAPTER 2

Rex

After a couple of days, I was able to walk without limping. I went over to Owen's. Nick was there too.

"How about a game of cricket?" suggested Owen.

"Yeah," said Nick, "I'm keen."

"How about you, Nathan? Fancy a game?"

"OK," I replied.

Then I had second thoughts. "What will
we do if the ball goes over the fence?"

"Out for six," answered Owen.

"Yeah ... but who gets the ball?" I asked.

"Whoever hits it," Owen said.

I wasn't too keen on this. The fence was a high wooden fence with rails on one side only. On the other side there was nothing to climb up on. And Rex! Rex was a big dog — a German shepherd.

"No fancy lob shots," I said to myself when I went in to bat. I tried to play each ball low. But within three deliveries the ball caught an edge and lofted high into the air. "Oh, no!" I groaned.

We climbed onto the fence and looked into the garden. The ball was in the middle of the lawn. And there was Rex in his kennel at the end of the garden. He seemed to be asleep.

"Did you know, Nathan, that Rex hasn't been fed for two weeks?" said Owen.

"Really! How come?"

"Mr Roach reckons Rex has to learn to eat raw meat. They've stopped giving him cooked food."

"Owen's just kidding, Nathan," laughed Nick. "Rex is really gentle."

"Oh ..." I said.

"Well," said Owen, "are you going to get the ball?"

"Keep your voice down," I whispered. "Rex might wake up."

"You're not scared of dogs, are you?" asked Owen.

"No ... well ... I am a bit," I said.

"Just sneak in and get the ball. Rex won't wake up," said Owen.

"You'll be all right," said Nick and Owen together. "Go on ..."

I stayed where I was.

At this point Rex decided to wake up. He strolled out into the sunshine and stretched. Nick called out, "Rex!" and he bounded over, barking ferociously.

I stayed on top of the fence. The last time these two dared me into something, I nearly broke my ankle.

"Go on, Nathan. You hit the ball over. You have to get it," said Nick.

"I'll get it," said Owen.

Owen dropped down into the yard. Rex
stopped barking. "Hi Rexy boy!" said Owen.
"Good fella!" The dog started wagging his
tail. He rolled onto his back and let
Owen scratch his belly.

"You know what you are?" said Owen, as he pulled himself back over the fence. "You're a chicken. That's what you are."

We started playing cricket again, but it wasn't fun anymore.

CHAPTER 3

The Zipper

The next day was a Saturday and I had to help Dad. "I'm taking a load of junk to the tip," he said. "You can help me load it all up."

There was a lot of old stuff under the house, and everything was covered in a thick layer of dust. I helped Dad carry out stacks of old books and jars, and an old rusty bed.

Then we dragged Dad's old go-cart out into the sunlight. It was really heavy. It had a coffin-shaped body made of sheets of iron nailed over a wooden frame. Dad wiped some dust away. 'The Zipper' was painted on the side.

"I made this with your Uncle Steve when I was about your age," said Dad smiling. "This was the fastest thing around. All the kids used to have races down Birdy Street."

"You actually drove this down Birdy Street?" I gasped.

He lifted up the back of the go-cart.
"Come on," he said, "grab an end."

"You're not taking it to the tip, are you?"
I said. "Can't we keep it?"

Dad shook his head. "Too dangerous,"
he said.

I wiped off more dust. "Look at this!"
I said, pointing at the yellow and red
flames painted along each side. "Cool!"

"Please Dad, I won't drive it. I promise."

Dad thought for a moment. "OK, you can
keep it. But don't drive it on the road."

A couple of days later, Owen and Nick
came round to my place. I was out the
back working on The Zipper. I could see
they were impressed.

"What do you think?" I asked.

"Cool!" they said.

"How fast does it go?" Nick moved closer.

"Pretty fast, I reckon," I grinned.

"Well, let's give it a run. Let's go down Birdy Street," said Nick.

"Cool!" said Owen. "Birdy Street would be fantastic! Let's go."

"Hang on, guys." I didn't like the way
things were moving.

They looked at me.

"It hasn't got any brakes," I said.

"So what!"

"We don't need brakes, do we Nick?"
said Owen.

"No," said Nick. "This doesn't have brakes,"
and he held up his skateboard.

"My dad would kill me if he knew I was driving it on the road," I said. "I promised him I wouldn't drive it."

They looked at each other. "Your dad doesn't have to know."

I looked at The Zipper. It looked like one of those old-fashioned racing cars.

"Nathan," said Owen shaking his head at me, "what is the point of having a go-cart if you're too scared to drive it?"

"Are you chickening out again, Nathan?"
Nick joined in.

My face went hot. They weren't going
to let me forget last time.

I made up my mind. "I suppose one drive won't hurt."

CHAPTER  4

Birdy Street

"OK, guys," I said when we reached the top of Birdy Street. It was the steepest, longest, meanest hill in the neighbourhood. "Who wants to go first?"

Owen and Nick looked at each other.

"Hey. It's YOUR go-cart, Nathan!" they said together.

"I reckon it's safe," I said.

"If you're so sure it's safe, you should be the one who goes first," said Nick.

"Yeah," said Owen. "Or are you going to chicken out again?"

There was a long silence. They were both staring at me.

I felt my heart beating faster. "OK!" I said, and strapped on my freshly painted Zipper helmet. I squeezed into the seat.

"You'll be all right," Owen patted me on the back. "We'll follow you down on our skateboards."

"No worries," said Nick, and he winked at Owen.

The two of them pushed me off and I gathered speed. I looked back. They were following me on their skateboards but they were zigzagging.

I tried to slow down by zigzagging. The
Zipper was steered by a rope attached
to the front axle. I pulled lightly and
nearly swerved out of control, into a pole.

"Help me, you guys!" I shouted. But Nick and Owen had already hopped off their skateboards and were left far behind.

Soon I was going very fast.

45

I tried slowing down by dragging my feet along the road. It made zero difference. The Zipper was just too heavy. It kept going faster and faster. It started shaking and rattling. It felt like it would fly apart.

"Yeeearrrgh!!!!" I screamed, as I sped down the steepest part of the hill. "How fast is this thing going to go?"

It still kept gaining speed. I thought maybe I should jump out, but it was too late for that. I should have put a parachute on the back to slow it down.

I saw a woman up ahead getting into her car.

"What if she backs out onto the road?" I groaned. I clung to the rope. The wheels were wobbling like crazy. They had seemed OK when I had oiled them, but now I wasn't sure. "What if a wheel falls off?" I thought. "Yikes!"

My eyes were streaming from the wind. Through the tears I could see that the road ahead was clear. It was a wonderful feeling. The terror stopped and I started to enjoy myself. The Zipper had stopped shaking and was riding smoothly.

"Phew! I'm going to make it!" I thought.

"Yahoooooooo!!"

The Zipper shot towards the bottom of Birdy Street like a rocket.

The Zipper was cruising beautifully now. As I got closer to the bottom it slowed a little and a car drove up beside me. I grinned at the woman in the passenger seat. I felt very proud of myself.

She wound down the window and shouted, "Pull over."

It was then that I noticed she was wearing a police uniform. "Police! Oh no!" I groaned. "I can't," I shouted back.

"Pull over," she called again, and pointed at the kerb.

"No brakes."

The road became flatter. I tried dragging my feet on the road and The Zipper finally slowed to a halt. The police car pulled over in front of me. Two constables got out and walked back to me.

"We clocked you at 40 miles per hour on the radar gun," said the policewoman. She took out her notebook and pen. "What is your reason for exceeding the speed limit?"

I couldn't answer.

"You were lucky the police let you off with a warning, Nathan," said Dad that night. He had finally broken his angry silence. "You were lucky you didn't break your neck." He carried on, "I thought you had more sense. Didn't you realise how badly you could have hurt yourself?"

"I dunno."

"I'm disappointed in you." He looked me in the eye. "What on earth made you do such a stupid, reckless thing?"

"I didn't want Owen and Nick to think I was a coward."

"Oh ... I see," said Dad nodding. "I should never have let you keep The Zipper in the first place. Next time you're dared by your mates to do something stupid, just walk away. Will you do that?"

"Walk away? Yes ... er ... probably," I said.

Dad grinned, "Probably? What do you mean, 'probably'?" He laughed and gave me a big hug.

GLOSSARY

axle
the bar on which
the wheels rotate

cruising
moving smoothly and easily

disbelief
unable to believe

ferociously
very fiercely

parachute
a big balloon of material
that slows things down

perched
sitting on top of

sprain
to hurt your ankle
without breaking it

streaming
flowing steadily

terror
intense fear

zigzagging
moving one way and
then the other way

David Dickson

What is your favourite thing?

A hot pie on a cold day.

What do you like about yourself?

That I have some friends.

Why did the cow jump over the moon?

It leant against an electric fence.

What is your best midnight snack?

A grilled loin chop with pepper and salt.